go *after*
THE LIFE U
want

This planner belongs to:

@

\#

www.

My mantra:

Move into your day.
Be mindful of how you *feel*.
Master your *passion*.
When you do these things
and do them often,
you will truly be the leader
of your *destiny*

How to Use the Good Morning Good Life Planner

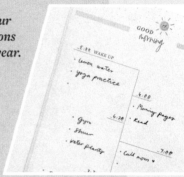

Set your intentions for the year.

Schedule your morning and night-time routines regularly.

*Keep track of your progress every day, week, and month. Write everything down. Ideas, connections, tasks, events, and goals. What gets measured gets done. Use your calendars and lists to prove to yourself that you **can** follow through.*

Make sure you hit your movement, mindfulness, and mastery everyday to go after the life you want!

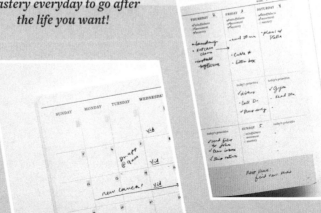

When you are unapologetically clear on why you want to achieve your goals, you will have taken the first necessary steps toward self awareness that will propel you forward every day.

WHAT IS YOUR *Why!*

2020

JANUARY

S	M	T	W	T	F	S
			1	2	3	4
5	6	7	8	9	10	11
12	13	14	15	16	17	18
19	20	21	22	23	24	25
26	27	28	29	30	31	

FEBRUARY

S	M	T	W	T	F	S
						1
2	3	4	5	6	7	8
9	10	11	12	13	14	15
16	17	18	19	20	21	22
23	24	25	26	27	28	29

MARCH

S	M	T	W	T	F	S
1	2	3	4	5	6	7
8	9	10	11	12	13	14
15	16	17	18	19	20	21
22	23	24	25	26	27	28
29	30	31				

APRIL

S	M	T	W	T	F	S
			1	2	3	4
5	6	7	8	9	10	11
12	13	14	15	16	17	18
19	20	21	22	23	24	25
26	27	28	29	30		

MAY

S	M	T	W	T	F	S
					1	2
3	4	5	6	7	8	9
10	11	12	13	14	15	16
17	18	19	20	21	22	23
24	25	26	27	28	29	30
31						

JUNE

S	M	T	W	T	F	S
	1	2	3	4	5	6
7	8	9	10	11	12	13
14	15	16	17	18	19	20
21	22	23	24	25	26	27
28	29	30				

JULY

S	M	T	W	T	F	S
			1	2	3	4
5	6	7	8	9	10	11
12	13	14	15	16	17	18
19	20	21	22	23	24	25
26	27	28	29	30	31	

AUGUST

S	M	T	W	T	F	S
						1
2	3	4	5	6	7	8
9	10	11	12	13	14	15
16	17	18	19	20	21	22
23	24	25	26	27	28	29
30	31					

SEPTEMBER

S	M	T	W	T	F	S
		1	2	3	4	5
6	7	8	9	10	11	12
13	14	15	16	17	18	19
20	21	22	23	24	25	26
27	28	29	30			

OCTOBER

S	M	T	W	T	F	S
				1	2	3
4	5	6	7	8	9	10
11	12	13	14	15	16	17
18	19	20	21	22	23	24
25	26	27	28	29	30	31

NOVEMBER

S	M	T	W	T	F	S
1	2	3	4	5	6	7
8	9	10	11	12	13	14
15	16	17	18	19	20	21
22	23	24	25	26	27	28
29	30					

DECEMBER

S	M	T	W	T	F	S
		1	2	3	4	5
6	7	8	9	10	11	12
13	14	15	16	17	18	19
20	21	22	23	24	25	26
27	28	29	30	31		

2021

JANUARY

S	M	T	W	T	F	S
					1	2
3	4	5	6	7	8	9
10	11	12	13	14	15	16
17	18	19	20	21	22	23
24	25	26	27	28	29	30
31						

FEBRUARY

S	M	T	W	T	F	S
	1	2	3	4	5	6
7	8	9	10	11	12	13
14	15	16	17	18	19	20
21	22	23	24	24	26	27
28						

MARCH

S	M	T	W	T	F	S
	1	2	3	4	5	6
7	8	9	19	11	12	13
14	15	16	17	18	19	20
21	22	23	24	25	26	27
28	29	30	31			

APRIL

S	M	T	W	T	F	S
				1	2	3
4	5	6	7	8	9	10
11	12	13	14	15	16	17
18	19	20	21	22	23	24
25	26	27	28	29	30	

MAY

S	M	T	W	T	F	S
						1
2	3	4	5	6	7	8
9	10	11	12	13	14	15
16	17	18	19	20	21	22
23	24	25	26	27	28	29
30	31					

JUNE

S	M	T	W	T	F	S
		1	2	3	4	5
6	7	8	9	10	11	12
13	14	15	16	17	18	19
20	21	22	23	24	25	26
27	28	29	30			

JULY

S	M	T	W	T	F	S
				1	2	3
4	5	6	7	8	9	10
11	12	13	14	15	16	17
18	19	20	21	22	23	24
25	26	27	28	29	30	31

AUGUST

S	M	T	W	T	F	S
1	2	3	4	5	6	7
8	9	10	11	12	13	14
15	16	17	18	19	20	21
22	23	24	25	26	27	28
29	30	31				

SEPTEMBER

S	M	T	W	T	F	S
			1	2	3	4
5	6	7	8	9	10	11
12	13	14	15	16	17	18
19	20	21	22	23	24	25
26	27	28	29	30	31	

OCTOBER

S	M	T	W	T	F	S
					1	2
3	4	5	6	7	8	9
10	11	12	13	14	15	16
17	18	19	20	21	22	23
24	25	26	27	28	29	30
31						

NOVEMBER

S	M	T	W	T	F	S
	1	2	3	4	5	6
7	8	9	10	11	12	13
14	15	16	17	18	19	20
21	22	23	24	25	26	27
28	29	30				

DECEMBER

S	M	T	W	T	F	S
			1	2	3	4
5	6	7	8	9	10	11
12	13	14	15	16	17	18
19	20	21	22	23	24	25
26	27	28	29	30	31	

IMPORTANT EVENTS

JANUARY

FEBRUARY

MARCH

APRIL

MAY

JUNE

JULY

AUGUST

SEPTEMBER

OCTOBER

NOVEMBER

DECEMBER

*Set your intentions for the year by visualizing the
writing goals that will get you the life you want.*

health

- Drink lemon water, daily!
- Make movement a daily action. — PVolve ★
- <u>Begin</u> dental plan.
-

career

- <u>Daily</u> deliverables completed.
- Start (and finish) classes to boost my resume
- Organize my office for better productivity

spiritual

- Start morning pages and do them daily
- 5 min. journal for gratitude.
- meditate

relationships

- Do something together at <u>least</u> 1x per. month.
- Be trusting.

GOOD
morning

_5:00_ *WAKE UP*

- Skin care
- Lemon Water
- Morning Pages

5:20

- 5 min. Journal
- Read

5:30

- Meditate
- Goal Review
- movement! 5:40-6:10

6:30

- Write something?
- Visualize
- Research my passion

7:00

Jayda Not Home
- Foreign Language practice?
- Re-write passage

Jayda Home
- Wake her up
- Dressed, Fed + Ready

__:__

"Eat the Frog"

__:__

__:__

__:__

__:__

__:__

__:__ *GO TO BED*

GOOD  *night*

SUNDAY	MONDAY	TUESDAY	WEDNESDAY
1	2	3	4
8	9	10	11
15	16	17	18
22	23	24	25
29	30	31	

THURSDAY	FRIDAY	SATURDAY	
5	6	7	
12	13	14	
19	20	21	
26	27	28	

MONTHLY GOALS FOR

*Make your annual goals more achievable with smaller steps
every month. Set those intentions here.*

GOOD MORNING MOMENTS

*When you capture these 3 moments every morning
you will consistently move toward the life you want!*

Movement

Mindfulness

Mastery

Events & Birthdays

/ /

/ /

/ /

/ /

/ /

/ /

/ /

People to reach out to

Reading

Watching

Planning

Learning

Ideas

MONDAY

- ○ movement
- ○ mindfulness
- ○ mastery

TUESDAY

- ○ movement
- ○ mindfulness
- ○ mastery

WEDNESDAY

- ○ movement
- ○ mindfulness
- ○ mastery

today's priorities

- •
- •
- •

today's priorities

- •
- •
- •

today's priorities

- •
- •
- •

**What time are
you going to bed**

tonight?

good night

THURSDAY

○ *movement*
○ *mindfulness*
○ *mastery*

FRIDAY

○ *movement*
○ *mindfulness*
○ *mastery*

SATURDAY

○ *movement*
○ *mindfulness*
○ *mastery*

today's priorities

•

•

•

today's priorities

•

•

•

today's priorities

•

•

•

SUNDAY

○ *movement*
○ *mindfulness*
○ *mastery*

today's priorities

•

•

•

MONDAY

○ movement
○ mindfulness
○ mastery

TUESDAY

○ movement
○ mindfulness
○ mastery

WEDNESDAY

○ movement
○ mindfulness
○ mastery

today's priorities

•

•

•

today's priorities

•

•

•

today's priorities

•

•

•

**What time are
you going to bed
tonight?**

good night

THURSDAY ____

○ *movement*
○ *mindfulness*
○ *mastery*

FRIDAY ____

○ *movement*
○ *mindfulness*
○ *mastery*

SATURDAY ____

○ *movement*
○ *mindfulness*
○ *mastery*

today's priorities

•

•

•

today's priorities

•

•

•

today's priorities

•

•

•

SUNDAY ____

○ *movement*
○ *mindfulness*
○ *mastery*

today's priorities

•

•

•

MONDAY _____

○ movement
○ mindfulness
○ mastery

TUESDAY _____

○ movement
○ mindfulness
○ mastery

WEDNESDAY _____

○ movement
○ mindfulness
○ mastery

today's priorities

•

•

•

today's priorities

•

•

•

today's priorities

•

•

•

*What time are
you going to bed*

tonight?

good

night

THURSDAY ___

○ *movement*
○ *mindfulness*
○ *mastery*

FRIDAY ___

○ *movement*
○ *mindfulness*
○ *mastery*

SATURDAY ___

○ *movement*
○ *mindfulness*
○ *mastery*

today's priorities

•

•

•

today's priorities

•

•

•

today's priorities

•

•

•

SUNDAY ___

○ *movement*
○ *mindfulness*
○ *mastery*

today's priorities

•

•

•

MONDAY ___

○ movement
○ mindfulness
○ mastery

TUESDAY ___

○ movement
○ mindfulness
○ mastery

WEDNESDAY ___

○ movement
○ mindfulness
○ mastery

today's priorities

•

•

•

today's priorities

•

•

•

today's priorities

•

•

•

*What time are
you going to bed*

tonight?

good

night

THURSDAY

○ *movement*
○ *mindfulness*
○ *mastery*

FRIDAY

○ *movement*
○ *mindfulness*
○ *mastery*

today's priorities

•

•

•

SATURDAY

○ *movement*
○ *mindfulness*
○ *mastery*

today's priorities

•

•

•

today's priorities

•

•

•

SUNDAY

○ *movement*
○ *mindfulness*
○ *mastery*

today's priorities

•

•

•

MONDAY

○ movement
○ mindfulness
○ mastery

TUESDAY

○ movement
○ mindfulness
○ mastery

WEDNESDAY

○ movement
○ mindfulness
○ mastery

today's priorities

•

•

•

today's priorities

•

•

•

today's priorities

•

•

•

**What time are
you going to bed**

tonight?

good night

THURSDAY ___

○ *movement*
○ *mindfulness*
○ *mastery*

FRIDAY ___

○ *movement*
○ *mindfulness*
○ *mastery*

SATURDAY ___

○ *movement*
○ *mindfulness*
○ *mastery*

today's priorities

•

•

•

today's priorities

•

•

•

today's priorities

•

•

•

SUNDAY ___

○ *movement*
○ *mindfulness*
○ *mastery*

today's priorities

•

•

•

reflection

reflection

SUNDAY	MONDAY	TUESDAY	WEDNESDAY

THURSDAY   **FRIDAY**   **SATURDAY**

MONTHLY GOALS FOR _____

*Make your annual goals more achievable with smaller steps
every month. Set those intentions here.*

GOOD MORNING MOMENTS

*When you capture these 3 moments every morning
you will consistently move toward the life you want!*

Movement _____

_____

Mindfulness

Mastery _____

Events & Birthdays

/ /

/ /

/ /

/ /

/ /

/ /

/ /

People to reach out to

Reading

Watching

Planning

Learning

Ideas

MONDAY ____

- ○ movement
- ○ mindfulness
- ○ mastery

TUESDAY ____

- ○ movement
- ○ mindfulness
- ○ mastery

WEDNESDAY ____

- ○ movement
- ○ mindfulness
- ○ mastery

today's priorities

- •

- •

- •

today's priorities

- •

- •

- •

today's priorities

- •

- •

- •

**What time are
you going to bed
tonight?**

*good
night*

THURSDAY ___

○ *movement*
○ *mindfulness*
○ *mastery*

FRIDAY ___

○ *movement*
○ *mindfulness*
○ *mastery*

SATURDAY ___

○ *movement*
○ *mindfulness*
○ *mastery*

today's priorities

•

•

•

today's priorities

•

•

•

today's priorities

•

•

•

SUNDAY ___

○ *movement*
○ *mindfulness*
○ *mastery*

today's priorities

•

•

•

MONDAY ____

○ movement
○ mindfulness
○ mastery

TUESDAY ____

○ movement
○ mindfulness
○ mastery

WEDNESDAY ____

○ movement
○ mindfulness
○ mastery

today's priorities

•

•

•

today's priorities

•

•

•

today's priorities

•

•

•

*What time are
you going to bed*

tonight?

good night

THURSDAY ___

○ *movement*
○ *mindfulness*
○ *mastery*

FRIDAY ___

○ *movement*
○ *mindfulness*
○ *mastery*

SATURDAY ___

○ *movement*
○ *mindfulness*
○ *mastery*

today's priorities

•

•

•

today's priorities

•

•

•

today's priorities

•

•

•

SUNDAY ___

○ *movement*
○ *mindfulness*
○ *mastery*

today's priorities

•

•

•

MONDAY ____

○ *movement*
○ *mindfulness*
○ *mastery*

TUESDAY ____

○ *movement*
○ *mindfulness*
○ *mastery*

WEDNESDAY ____

○ *movement*
○ *mindfulness*
○ *mastery*

today's priorities

●

●

●

today's priorities

●

●

●

today's priorities

●

●

●

**What time are
you going to bed**

tonight?

good night

THURSDAY ____

○ *movement*
○ *mindfulness*
○ *mastery*

FRIDAY ____

○ *movement*
○ *mindfulness*
○ *mastery*

SATURDAY ____

○ *movement*
○ *mindfulness*
○ *mastery*

today's priorities

•

•

•

today's priorities

•

•

•

today's priorities

•

•

•

SUNDAY ____

○ *movement*
○ *mindfulness*
○ *mastery*

today's priorities

•

•

•

MONDAY	TUESDAY	WEDNESDAY
○ movement	○ movement	○ movement
○ mindfulness	○ mindfulness	○ mindfulness
○ mastery	○ mastery	○ mastery

today's priorities	today's priorities	today's priorities
•	•	•
•	•	•
•	•	•

What time are you going to bed

tonight?

good night

THURSDAY ___

○ *movement*
○ *mindfulness*
○ *mastery*

FRIDAY ___

○ *movement*
○ *mindfulness*
○ *mastery*

SATURDAY ___

○ *movement*
○ *mindfulness*
○ *mastery*

today's priorities

●

●

●

today's priorities

●

●

●

today's priorities

●

●

●

SUNDAY ___

○ *movement*
○ *mindfulness*
○ *mastery*

today's priorities

●

●

●

reflection

reflection

41

SUNDAY	MONDAY	TUESDAY	WEDNESDAY

THURSDAY   **FRIDAY**   **SATURDAY**

MONTHLY GOALS FOR _____

Make your annual goals more achievable with smaller steps
every month. Set those intentions here.

GOOD MORNING MOMENTS

When you capture these 3 moments every morning
you will consistently move toward the life you want!

Movement _____

_____

Mindfulness

Mastery _____

Events & Birthdays

/   /

/   /

/   /

/   /

/   /

/   /

/   /

People to reach out to

Reading

Watching

Planning

Learning

Ideas

45

MONDAY ____

○ movement
○ mindfulness
○ mastery

TUESDAY ____

○ movement
○ mindfulness
○ mastery

WEDNESDAY ____

○ movement
○ mindfulness
○ mastery

today's priorities

•

•

•

today's priorities

•

•

•

today's priorities

•

•

•

**What time are
you going to bed**

tonight?

good

night

THURSDAY ___

- ○ *movement*
- ○ *mindfulness*
- ○ *mastery*

FRIDAY ___

- ○ *movement*
- ○ *mindfulness*
- ○ *mastery*

SATURDAY ___

- ○ *movement*
- ○ *mindfulness*
- ○ *mastery*

today's priorities

- •
- •
- •

today's priorities

- •
- •
- •

today's priorities

- •
- •
- •

SUNDAY ___

- ○ *movement*
- ○ *mindfulness*
- ○ *mastery*

today's priorities

- •
- •
- •

MONDAY

○ movement
○ mindfulness
○ mastery

TUESDAY

○ movement
○ mindfulness
○ mastery

WEDNESDAY

○ movement
○ mindfulness
○ mastery

today's priorities

•

•

•

today's priorities

•

•

•

today's priorities

•

•

•

*What time are
you going to bed*

tonight?

good night

THURSDAY ___

○ *movement*
○ *mindfulness*
○ *mastery*

FRIDAY ___

○ *movement*
○ *mindfulness*
○ *mastery*

SATURDAY ___

○ *movement*
○ *mindfulness*
○ *mastery*

today's priorities

•

•

•

today's priorities

•

•

•

today's priorities

•

•

•

SUNDAY ___

○ *movement*
○ *mindfulness*
○ *mastery*

today's priorities

•

•

•

MONDAY ____

○ movement
○ mindfulness
○ mastery

TUESDAY ____

○ movement
○ mindfulness
○ mastery

WEDNESDAY ____

○ movement
○ mindfulness
○ mastery

today's priorities

•

•

•

today's priorities

•

•

•

today's priorities

•

•

•

What time are you going to bed

tonight?

good night

THURSDAY ___

○ *movement*
○ *mindfulness*
○ *mastery*

FRIDAY ___

○ *movement*
○ *mindfulness*
○ *mastery*

SATURDAY ___

○ *movement*
○ *mindfulness*
○ *mastery*

today's priorities

•

•

•

today's priorities

•

•

•

today's priorities

•

•

•

SUNDAY ___

○ *movement*
○ *mindfulness*
○ *mastery*

today's priorities

•

•

•

MONDAY ___

○ movement
○ mindfulness
○ mastery

TUESDAY ___

○ movement
○ mindfulness
○ mastery

WEDNESDAY ___

○ movement
○ mindfulness
○ mastery

today's priorities

·

·

·

today's priorities

·

·

·

today's priorities

·

·

·

What time are you going to bed

tonight?

good night

THURSDAY ___

- ○ *movement*
- ○ *mindfulness*
- ○ *mastery*

FRIDAY ___

- ○ *movement*
- ○ *mindfulness*
- ○ *mastery*

SATURDAY ___

- ○ *movement*
- ○ *mindfulness*
- ○ *mastery*

today's priorities

- •
- •
- •

today's priorities

- •
- •
- •

today's priorities

- •
- •
- •

SUNDAY ___

- ○ *movement*
- ○ *mindfulness*
- ○ *mastery*

today's priorities

- •
- •
- •

reflection

reflection

SUNDAY	MONDAY	TUESDAY	WEDNESDAY

THURSDAY   **FRIDAY**   **SATURDAY**

MONTHLY GOALS FOR _____

*Make your annual goals more achievable with smaller steps
every month. Set those intentions here.*

GOOD MORNING MOMENTS

*When you capture these 3 moments every morning
you will consistently move toward the life you want!*

Movement _____

_____

Mindfulness

Mastery _____

Events & Birthdays

/ /

/ /

/ /

/ /

/ /

/ /

/ /

People to reach out to

Reading

Watching

Planning

Learning

Ideas

MONDAY _____

○ movement
○ mindfulness
○ mastery

TUESDAY _____

○ movement
○ mindfulness
○ mastery

WEDNESDAY _____

○ movement
○ mindfulness
○ mastery

today's priorities

•

•

•

today's priorities

•

•

•

today's priorities

•

•

•

*What time are
you going to bed*

tonight?

good night

THURSDAY ___

○ *movement*
○ *mindfulness*
○ *mastery*

FRIDAY ___

○ *movement*
○ *mindfulness*
○ *mastery*

SATURDAY ___

○ *movement*
○ *mindfulness*
○ *mastery*

today's priorities

•

•

•

today's priorities

•

•

•

today's priorities

•

•

•

SUNDAY ___

○ *movement*
○ *mindfulness*
○ *mastery*

today's priorities

•

•

•

MONDAY ___

- ○ movement
- ○ mindfulness
- ○ mastery

TUESDAY ___

- ○ movement
- ○ mindfulness
- ○ mastery

WEDNESDAY ___

- ○ movement
- ○ mindfulness
- ○ mastery

today's priorities

- •
- •
- •

today's priorities

- •
- •
- •

today's priorities

- •
- •
- •

What time are you going to bed tonight?

good night

THURSDAY _____

○ *movement*
○ *mindfulness*
○ *mastery*

FRIDAY _____

○ *movement*
○ *mindfulness*
○ *mastery*

SATURDAY _____

○ *movement*
○ *mindfulness*
○ *mastery*

today's priorities

•

•

•

today's priorities

•

•

•

today's priorities

•

•

•

SUNDAY _____

○ *movement*
○ *mindfulness*
○ *mastery*

today's priorities

•

•

•

MONDAY ___

○ movement
○ mindfulness
○ mastery

TUESDAY ___

○ movement
○ mindfulness
○ mastery

WEDNESDAY ___

○ movement
○ mindfulness
○ mastery

today's priorities

•

•

•

today's priorities

•

•

•

today's priorities

•

•

•

*What time are
you going to bed*

tonight?

good
night

THURSDAY _____

○ *movement*
○ *mindfulness*
○ *mastery*

FRIDAY _____

○ *movement*
○ *mindfulness*
○ *mastery*

SATURDAY _____

○ *movement*
○ *mindfulness*
○ *mastery*

today's priorities

●

●

●

today's priorities

●

●

●

today's priorities

●

●

●

SUNDAY _____

○ *movement*
○ *mindfulness*
○ *mastery*

today's priorities

●

●

●

MONDAY ____

○ movement
○ mindfulness
○ mastery

TUESDAY ____

○ movement
○ mindfulness
○ mastery

WEDNESDAY ____

○ movement
○ mindfulness
○ mastery

today's priorities

•

•

•

today's priorities

•

•

•

today's priorities

•

•

•

*What time are
you going to bed*

tonight?

good
night

THURSDAY ___

○ *movement*
○ *mindfulness*
○ *mastery*

FRIDAY ___

○ *movement*
○ *mindfulness*
○ *mastery*

SATURDAY ___

○ *movement*
○ *mindfulness*
○ *mastery*

today's priorities

•

•

•

today's priorities

•

•

•

today's priorities

•

•

•

SUNDAY ___

○ *movement*
○ *mindfulness*
○ *mastery*

today's priorities

•

•

•

reflection

reflection

SUNDAY	MONDAY	TUESDAY	WEDNESDAY

THURSDAY   **FRIDAY**   **SATURDAY**

MONTHLY GOALS FOR _____

*Make your annual goals more achievable with smaller steps
every month. Set those intentions here.*

GOOD MORNING MOMENTS

*When you capture these 3 moments every morning
you will consistently move toward the life you want!*

Movement _____

_____

_____ Mindfulness

Mastery _____

_____

Events & Birthdays

/ /

/ /

/ /

/ /

/ /

/ /

/ /

People to reach out to

Reading

Watching

Planning

Learning

Ideas

MONDAY ___

○ movement
○ mindfulness
○ mastery

TUESDAY ___

○ movement
○ mindfulness
○ mastery

WEDNESDAY ___

○ movement
○ mindfulness
○ mastery

today's priorities

•

•

•

today's priorities

•

•

•

today's priorities

•

•

•

What time are you going to bed

tonight?

good night

THURSDAY ___

○ *movement*
○ *mindfulness*
○ *mastery*

FRIDAY ___

○ *movement*
○ *mindfulness*
○ *mastery*

SATURDAY ___

○ *movement*
○ *mindfulness*
○ *mastery*

today's priorities

•

•

•

today's priorities

•

•

•

today's priorities

•

•

•

SUNDAY ___

○ *movement*
○ *mindfulness*
○ *mastery*

today's priorities

•

•

•

MONDAY ___

○ movement
○ mindfulness
○ mastery

TUESDAY ___

○ movement
○ mindfulness
○ mastery

WEDNESDAY ___

○ movement
○ mindfulness
○ mastery

today's priorities

•

•

•

today's priorities

•

•

•

today's priorities

•

•

•

*What time are
you going to bed*

tonight?

good night

THURSDAY ____

- ○ *movement*
- ○ *mindfulness*
- ○ *mastery*

FRIDAY ____

- ○ *movement*
- ○ *mindfulness*
- ○ *mastery*

SATURDAY ____

- ○ *movement*
- ○ *mindfulness*
- ○ *mastery*

today's priorities

- •
- •
- •

today's priorities

- •
- •
- •

today's priorities

- •
- •
- •

SUNDAY ____

- ○ *movement*
- ○ *mindfulness*
- ○ *mastery*

today's priorities

- •
- •
- •

MONDAY _____	TUESDAY _____	WEDNESDAY _____
○ movement	○ movement	○ movement
○ mindfulness	○ mindfulness	○ mindfulness
○ mastery	○ mastery	○ mastery

today's priorities	today's priorities	today's priorities
•	•	•
•	•	•
•	•	•

*What time are
you going to bed*

tonight?

good
night

THURSDAY ___

○ *movement*
○ *mindfulness*
○ *mastery*

FRIDAY ___

○ *movement*
○ *mindfulness*
○ *mastery*

SATURDAY ___

○ *movement*
○ *mindfulness*
○ *mastery*

today's priorities

•

•

•

today's priorities

•

•

•

today's priorities

•

•

•

SUNDAY ___

○ *movement*
○ *mindfulness*
○ *mastery*

today's priorities

•

•

•

MONDAY ___

○ movement
○ mindfulness
○ mastery

TUESDAY ___

○ movement
○ mindfulness
○ mastery

WEDNESDAY ___

○ movement
○ mindfulness
○ mastery

today's priorities

•

•

•

today's priorities

•

•

•

today's priorities

•

•

•

*What time are
you going to bed*

tonight?

good

night

THURSDAY ___

○ *movement*
○ *mindfulness*
○ *mastery*

FRIDAY ___

○ *movement*
○ *mindfulness*
○ *mastery*

SATURDAY ___

○ *movement*
○ *mindfulness*
○ *mastery*

today's priorities

•

•

•

today's priorities

•

•

•

today's priorities

•

•

•

SUNDAY ___

○ *movement*
○ *mindfulness*
○ *mastery*

today's priorities

•

•

•

MONDAY ____

○ *movement*
○ *mindfulness*
○ *mastery*

TUESDAY ____

○ *movement*
○ *mindfulness*
○ *mastery*

WEDNESDAY ____

○ *movement*
○ *mindfulness*
○ *mastery*

today's priorities

•

•

•

today's priorities

•

•

•

today's priorities

•

•

•

**What time are
you going to bed**

tonight?

good
night

THURSDAY ___

○ *movement*
○ *mindfulness*
○ *mastery*

FRIDAY ___

○ *movement*
○ *mindfulness*
○ *mastery*

SATURDAY ___

○ *movement*
○ *mindfulness*
○ *mastery*

today's priorities

•

•

•

today's priorities

•

•

•

today's priorities

•

•

•

SUNDAY ___

○ *movement*
○ *mindfulness*
○ *mastery*

today's priorities

•

•

•

reflection

reflection

SUNDAY	MONDAY	TUESDAY	WEDNESDAY

THURSDAY   FRIDAY   SATURDAY

MONTHLY GOALS FOR _____

Make your annual goals more achievable with smaller steps
every month. Set those intentions here.

GOOD MORNING MOMENTS

When you capture these 3 moments every morning
you will consistently move toward the life you want!

Movement _____

Mindfulness _____

Mastery _____

Events & Birthdays

/ /

/ /

/ /

/ /

/ /

/ /

/ /

People to reach out to

Reading

Watching

Planning

Learning

Ideas

MONDAY ___

○ *movement*
○ *mindfulness*
○ *mastery*

TUESDAY ___

○ *movement*
○ *mindfulness*
○ *mastery*

WEDNESDAY ___

○ *movement*
○ *mindfulness*
○ *mastery*

today's priorities

•

•

•

today's priorities

•

•

•

today's priorities

•

•

•

*What time are
you going to bed*

tonight?

good night

THURSDAY ___

- ○ *movement*
- ○ *mindfulness*
- ○ *mastery*

FRIDAY ___

- ○ *movement*
- ○ *mindfulness*
- ○ *mastery*

SATURDAY ___

- ○ *movement*
- ○ *mindfulness*
- ○ *mastery*

today's priorities

- •
- •
- •

today's priorities

- •
- •
- •

today's priorities

- •
- •
- •

SUNDAY ___

- ○ *movement*
- ○ *mindfulness*
- ○ *mastery*

today's priorities

- •
- •
- •

MONDAY

- ○ *movement*
- ○ *mindfulness*
- ○ *mastery*

TUESDAY

- ○ *movement*
- ○ *mindfulness*
- ○ *mastery*

WEDNESDAY

- ○ *movement*
- ○ *mindfulness*
- ○ *mastery*

today's priorities

- •
- •
- •

today's priorities

- •
- •
- •

today's priorities

- •
- •
- •

What time are you going to bed tonight?

good night

THURSDAY ____

○ *movement*
○ *mindfulness*
○ *mastery*

FRIDAY ____

○ *movement*
○ *mindfulness*
○ *mastery*

today's priorities

•

•

•

SATURDAY ____

○ *movement*
○ *mindfulness*
○ *mastery*

today's priorities

•

•

•

today's priorities

•

•

•

SUNDAY ____

○ *movement*
○ *mindfulness*
○ *mastery*

today's priorities

•

•

•

MONDAY ___

○ movement
○ mindfulness
○ mastery

TUESDAY ___

○ movement
○ mindfulness
○ mastery

WEDNESDAY ___

○ movement
○ mindfulness
○ mastery

today's priorities

•

•

•

today's priorities

•

•

•

today's priorities

•

•

•

*What time are
you going to bed*

tonight?

good night

THURSDAY _____

○ *movement*
○ *mindfulness*
○ *mastery*

FRIDAY _____

○ *movement*
○ *mindfulness*
○ *mastery*

today's priorities

●

●

●

SATURDAY _____

○ *movement*
○ *mindfulness*
○ *mastery*

today's priorities

●

●

●

today's priorities

●

●

●

SUNDAY _____

○ *movement*
○ *mindfulness*
○ *mastery*

today's priorities

●

●

●

MONDAY _____

○ movement
○ mindfulness
○ mastery

TUESDAY _____

○ movement
○ mindfulness
○ mastery

WEDNESDAY _____

○ movement
○ mindfulness
○ mastery

today's priorities

•

•

•

today's priorities

•

•

•

today's priorities

•

•

•

*What time are
you going to bed*

tonight?

good
night

THURSDAY ___

○ *movement*
○ *mindfulness*
○ *mastery*

FRIDAY ___

○ *movement*
○ *mindfulness*
○ *mastery*

SATURDAY ___

○ *movement*
○ *mindfulness*
○ *mastery*

today's priorities

•

•

•

today's priorities

•

•

•

today's priorities

•

•

•

SUNDAY ___

○ *movement*
○ *mindfulness*
○ *mastery*

today's priorities

•

•

•

reflection

reflection

SUNDAY	MONDAY	TUESDAY	WEDNESDAY

THURSDAY   **FRIDAY**   **SATURDAY**

MONTHLY GOALS FOR

Make your annual goals more achievable with smaller steps
every month. Set those intentions here.

GOOD MORNING MOMENTS

When you capture these 3 moments every morning
you will consistently move toward the life you want!

Movement

Mindfulness

Mastery

Events & Birthdays

/ /

/ /

/ /

/ /

/ /

/ /

/ /

People to reach out to

Reading

Watching

Planning

Learning

Ideas

MONDAY _____

○ movement
○ mindfulness
○ mastery

TUESDAY _____

○ movement
○ mindfulness
○ mastery

WEDNESDAY _____

○ movement
○ mindfulness
○ mastery

today's priorities

•

•

•

today's priorities

•

•

•

today's priorities

•

•

•

*What time are
you going to bed*

tonight?

good

night

THURSDAY ___

- ○ *movement*
- ○ *mindfulness*
- ○ *mastery*

FRIDAY ___

- ○ *movement*
- ○ *mindfulness*
- ○ *mastery*

SATURDAY ___

- ○ *movement*
- ○ *mindfulness*
- ○ *mastery*

today's priorities

- •
- •
- •

today's priorities

- •
- •
- •

today's priorities

- •
- •
- •

SUNDAY ___

- ○ *movement*
- ○ *mindfulness*
- ○ *mastery*

today's priorities

- •
- •
- •

MONDAY ___

○ movement
○ mindfulness
○ mastery

TUESDAY ___

○ movement
○ mindfulness
○ mastery

WEDNESDAY ___

○ movement
○ mindfulness
○ mastery

today's priorities

•

•

•

today's priorities

•

•

•

today's priorities

•

•

•

What time are
you going to bed

tonight?

good
night

THURSDAY ___

○ movement
○ mindfulness
○ mastery

FRIDAY ___

○ movement
○ mindfulness
○ mastery

SATURDAY ___

○ movement
○ mindfulness
○ mastery

today's priorities

•

•

•

today's priorities

•

•

•

today's priorities

•

•

•

SUNDAY ___

○ movement
○ mindfulness
○ mastery

today's priorities

•

•

•

MONDAY ___

○ movement
○ mindfulness
○ mastery

TUESDAY ___

○ movement
○ mindfulness
○ mastery

WEDNESDAY ___

○ movement
○ mindfulness
○ mastery

today's priorities

•

•

•

today's priorities

•

•

•

today's priorities

•

•

•

*What time are
you going to bed*

tonight?

good
night

THURSDAY ___

○ *movement*
○ *mindfulness*
○ *mastery*

FRIDAY ___

○ *movement*
○ *mindfulness*
○ *mastery*

SATURDAY ___

○ *movement*
○ *mindfulness*
○ *mastery*

today's priorities

-
-
-

today's priorities

-
-
-

today's priorities

-
-
-

SUNDAY ___

○ *movement*
○ *mindfulness*
○ *mastery*

today's priorities

-
-
-

MONDAY

- ○ *movement*
- ○ *mindfulness*
- ○ *mastery*

TUESDAY

- ○ *movement*
- ○ *mindfulness*
- ○ *mastery*

WEDNESDAY

- ○ *movement*
- ○ *mindfulness*
- ○ *mastery*

today's priorities

- •

- •

- •

today's priorities

- •

- •

- •

today's priorities

- •

- •

- •

**What time are
you going to bed**

tonight?

good
night

THURSDAY ___

○ *movement*
○ *mindfulness*
○ *mastery*

FRIDAY ___

○ *movement*
○ *mindfulness*
○ *mastery*

SATURDAY ___

○ *movement*
○ *mindfulness*
○ *mastery*

today's priorities

•

•

•

today's priorities

•

•

•

today's priorities

•

•

•

SUNDAY ___

○ *movement*
○ *mindfulness*
○ *mastery*

today's priorities

•

•

•

MONDAY ____

○ *movement*
○ *mindfulness*
○ *mastery*

TUESDAY ____

○ *movement*
○ *mindfulness*
○ *mastery*

WEDNESDAY ____

○ *movement*
○ *mindfulness*
○ *mastery*

today's priorities

•

•

•

today's priorities

•

•

•

today's priorities

•

•

•

**What time are
you going to bed**

tonight?

good night

THURSDAY ____

○ *movement*
○ *mindfulness*
○ *mastery*

FRIDAY ____

○ *movement*
○ *mindfulness*
○ *mastery*

SATURDAY ____

○ *movement*
○ *mindfulness*
○ *mastery*

today's priorities

•

•

•

today's priorities

•

•

•

today's priorities

•

•

•

SUNDAY ____

○ *movement*
○ *mindfulness*
○ *mastery*

today's priorities

•

•

•

reflection

reflection

SUNDAY	MONDAY	TUESDAY	WEDNESDAY

THURSDAY **FRIDAY** **SATURDAY**

MONTHLY GOALS FOR _____

Make your annual goals more achievable with smaller steps
every month. Set those intentions here.

GOOD MORNING MOMENTS

When you capture these 3 moments every morning
you will consistently move toward the life you want!

Movement _____

_____

_____ Mindfulness

_____

Mastery _____

_____

Events & Birthdays

/ /

/ /

/ /

/ /

/ /

/ /

/ /

People to reach out to

Reading

Watching

Planning

Learning

Ideas

MONDAY

- ○ movement
- ○ mindfulness
- ○ mastery

TUESDAY

- ○ movement
- ○ mindfulness
- ○ mastery

WEDNESDAY

- ○ movement
- ○ mindfulness
- ○ mastery

today's priorities

- •

- •

- •

today's priorities

- •

- •

- •

today's priorities

- •

- •

- •

*What time are
you going to bed
tonight?*

good night

THURSDAY ____

○ *movement*
○ *mindfulness*
○ *mastery*

FRIDAY ____

○ *movement*
○ *mindfulness*
○ *mastery*

SATURDAY ____

○ *movement*
○ *mindfulness*
○ *mastery*

today's priorities

•

•

•

today's priorities

•

•

•

today's priorities

•

•

•

SUNDAY ____

○ *movement*
○ *mindfulness*
○ *mastery*

today's priorities

•

•

•

MONDAY ___

○ *movement*
○ *mindfulness*
○ *mastery*

TUESDAY ___

○ *movement*
○ *mindfulness*
○ *mastery*

WEDNESDAY ___

○ *movement*
○ *mindfulness*
○ *mastery*

today's priorities

•

•

•

today's priorities

•

•

•

today's priorities

•

•

•

What time are you going to bed tonight?

good night

THURSDAY ___

○ *movement*
○ *mindfulness*
○ *mastery*

FRIDAY ___

○ *movement*
○ *mindfulness*
○ *mastery*

today's priorities

•

•

•

SATURDAY ___

○ *movement*
○ *mindfulness*
○ *mastery*

today's priorities

•

•

•

today's priorities

•

•

•

SUNDAY ___

○ *movement*
○ *mindfulness*
○ *mastery*

today's priorities

•

•

•

MONDAY

○ movement
○ mindfulness
○ mastery

TUESDAY

○ movement
○ mindfulness
○ mastery

WEDNESDAY

○ movement
○ mindfulness
○ mastery

today's priorities

•

•

•

today's priorities

•

•

•

today's priorities

•

•

•

What time are
you going to bed

tonight?

good night

THURSDAY ___

○ *movement*
○ *mindfulness*
○ *mastery*

FRIDAY ___

○ *movement*
○ *mindfulness*
○ *mastery*

SATURDAY ___

○ *movement*
○ *mindfulness*
○ *mastery*

today's priorities

•

•

•

today's priorities

•

•

•

today's priorities

•

•

•

SUNDAY ___

○ *movement*
○ *mindfulness*
○ *mastery*

today's priorities

•

•

•

MONDAY ___

○ movement
○ mindfulness
○ mastery

TUESDAY ___

○ movement
○ mindfulness
○ mastery

WEDNESDAY ___

○ movement
○ mindfulness
○ mastery

today's priorities

•

•

•

today's priorities

•

•

•

today's priorities

•

•

•

*What time are
you going to bed*

tonight?

good night

THURSDAY _____

○ *movement*
○ *mindfulness*
○ *mastery*

FRIDAY _____

○ *movement*
○ *mindfulness*
○ *mastery*

SATURDAY _____

○ *movement*
○ *mindfulness*
○ *mastery*

today's priorities

•

•

•

today's priorities

•

•

•

today's priorities

•

•

•

SUNDAY _____

○ *movement*
○ *mindfulness*
○ *mastery*

today's priorities

•

•

•

reflection

reflection

SUNDAY	MONDAY	TUESDAY	WEDNESDAY

THURSDAY **FRIDAY** **SATURDAY**

MONTHLY GOALS FOR _____

*Make your annual goals more achievable with smaller steps
every month. Set those intentions here.*

GOOD MORNING MOMENTS

*When you capture these 3 moments every morning
you will consistently move toward the life you want!*

Movement _____

_____

Mindfulness

Mastery _____

Events & Birthdays

/　/

/　/

/　/

/　/

/　/

/　/

/　/

People to reach out to

Reading

Watching

Planning

Learning

Ideas

MONDAY ___

○ movement
○ mindfulness
○ mastery

TUESDAY ___

○ movement
○ mindfulness
○ mastery

WEDNESDAY ___

○ movement
○ mindfulness
○ mastery

today's priorities

•

•

•

today's priorities

•

•

•

today's priorities

•

•

•

**What time are
you going to bed**

tonight?

*good
night*

THURSDAY ___

○ *movement*
○ *mindfulness*
○ *mastery*

FRIDAY ___

○ *movement*
○ *mindfulness*
○ *mastery*

SATURDAY ___

○ *movement*
○ *mindfulness*
○ *mastery*

today's priorities

•

•

•

today's priorities

•

•

•

today's priorities

•

•

•

SUNDAY ___

○ *movement*
○ *mindfulness*
○ *mastery*

today's priorities

•

•

•

MONDAY ___

○ movement
○ mindfulness
○ mastery

TUESDAY ___

○ movement
○ mindfulness
○ mastery

WEDNESDAY ___

○ movement
○ mindfulness
○ mastery

today's priorities

•

•

•

today's priorities

•

•

•

today's priorities

•

•

•

*What time are
you going to bed*

tonight?

good night

THURSDAY ____

○ *movement*
○ *mindfulness*
○ *mastery*

FRIDAY ____

○ *movement*
○ *mindfulness*
○ *mastery*

SATURDAY ____

○ *movement*
○ *mindfulness*
○ *mastery*

today's priorities

•

•

•

today's priorities

•

•

•

today's priorities

•

•

•

SUNDAY ____

○ *movement*
○ *mindfulness*
○ *mastery*

today's priorities

•

•

•

MONDAY _____

- ○ *movement*
- ○ *mindfulness*
- ○ *mastery*

TUESDAY _____

- ○ *movement*
- ○ *mindfulness*
- ○ *mastery*

WEDNESDAY _____

- ○ *movement*
- ○ *mindfulness*
- ○ *mastery*

today's priorities

- •
- •
- •

today's priorities

- •
- •
- •

today's priorities

- •
- •
- •

What time are you going to bed

tonight?

good night

THURSDAY _____

○ *movement*
○ *mindfulness*
○ *mastery*

FRIDAY _____

○ *movement*
○ *mindfulness*
○ *mastery*

SATURDAY _____

○ *movement*
○ *mindfulness*
○ *mastery*

today's priorities

•

•

•

today's priorities

•

•

•

today's priorities

•

•

•

SUNDAY _____

○ *movement*
○ *mindfulness*
○ *mastery*

today's priorities

•

•

•

MONDAY

○ movement
○ mindfulness
○ mastery

TUESDAY

○ movement
○ mindfulness
○ mastery

WEDNESDAY

○ movement
○ mindfulness
○ mastery

today's priorities

•

•

•

today's priorities

•

•

•

today's priorities

•

•

•

**What time are
you going to bed**

tonight?

good
night

THURSDAY ___

○ *movement*
○ *mindfulness*
○ *mastery*

FRIDAY ___

○ *movement*
○ *mindfulness*
○ *mastery*

SATURDAY ___

○ *movement*
○ *mindfulness*
○ *mastery*

today's priorities

-
-
-

today's priorities

-
-
-

today's priorities

-
-
-

SUNDAY ___

○ *movement*
○ *mindfulness*
○ *mastery*

today's priorities

-
-
-

reflection

reflection

SUNDAY	MONDAY	TUESDAY	WEDNESDAY

THURSDAY	FRIDAY	SATURDAY	

MONTHLY GOALS FOR _____

*Make your annual goals more achievable with smaller steps
every month. Set those intentions here.*

GOOD MORNING MOMENTS

*When you capture these 3 moments every morning
you will consistently move toward the life you want!*

Movement _____

_____

Mindfulness

Mastery _____

Events & Birthdays

/   /

/   /

/   /

/   /

/   /

/   /

/   /

People to reach out to

Reading

Watching

Planning

Learning

Ideas

MONDAY

○ movement
○ mindfulness
○ mastery

TUESDAY

○ movement
○ mindfulness
○ mastery

WEDNESDAY

○ movement
○ mindfulness
○ mastery

today's priorities

•

•

•

today's priorities

•

•

•

today's priorities

•

•

•

*What time are
you going to bed*

tonight?

good night

THURSDAY ___

○ *movement*
○ *mindfulness*
○ *mastery*

FRIDAY ___

○ *movement*
○ *mindfulness*
○ *mastery*

SATURDAY ___

○ *movement*
○ *mindfulness*
○ *mastery*

today's priorities

•

•

•

today's priorities

•

•

•

today's priorities

•

•

•

SUNDAY ___

○ *movement*
○ *mindfulness*
○ *mastery*

today's priorities

•

•

•

MONDAY

○ movement
○ mindfulness
○ mastery

TUESDAY

○ movement
○ mindfulness
○ mastery

WEDNESDAY

○ movement
○ mindfulness
○ mastery

today's priorities

•

•

•

today's priorities

•

•

•

today's priorities

•

•

•

**What time are
you going to bed
tonight?**

good night

THURSDAY ____

○ *movement*
○ *mindfulness*
○ *mastery*

FRIDAY ____

○ *movement*
○ *mindfulness*
○ *mastery*

today's priorities

●

●

●

SATURDAY ____

○ *movement*
○ *mindfulness*
○ *mastery*

today's priorities

●

●

●

today's priorities

●

●

●

SUNDAY ____

○ *movement*
○ *mindfulness*
○ *mastery*

today's priorities

●

●

●

MONDAY

○ movement
○ mindfulness
○ mastery

TUESDAY

○ movement
○ mindfulness
○ mastery

WEDNESDAY

○ movement
○ mindfulness
○ mastery

today's priorities

•

•

•

today's priorities

•

•

•

today's priorities

•

•

•

What time are you going to bed tonight?

good night

THURSDAY ____

- ○ *movement*
- ○ *mindfulness*
- ○ *mastery*

FRIDAY ____

- ○ *movement*
- ○ *mindfulness*
- ○ *mastery*

SATURDAY ____

- ○ *movement*
- ○ *mindfulness*
- ○ *mastery*

today's priorities

- •

- •

- •

today's priorities

- •

- •

- •

today's priorities

- •

- •

- •

SUNDAY ____

- ○ *movement*
- ○ *mindfulness*
- ○ *mastery*

today's priorities

- •

- •

- •

MONDAY _____

○ *movement*
○ *mindfulness*
○ *mastery*

TUESDAY _____

○ *movement*
○ *mindfulness*
○ *mastery*

WEDNESDAY _____

○ *movement*
○ *mindfulness*
○ *mastery*

today's priorities

•

•

•

today's priorities

•

•

•

today's priorities

•

•

•

What time are you going to bed

tonight?

good night

THURSDAY ___

○ *movement*
○ *mindfulness*
○ *mastery*

FRIDAY ___

○ *movement*
○ *mindfulness*
○ *mastery*

SATURDAY ___

○ *movement*
○ *mindfulness*
○ *mastery*

today's priorities

•

•

•

today's priorities

•

•

•

today's priorities

•

•

•

SUNDAY ___

○ *movement*
○ *mindfulness*
○ *mastery*

today's priorities

•

•

•

MONDAY ____

- ○ *movement*
- ○ *mindfulness*
- ○ *mastery*

TUESDAY ____

- ○ *movement*
- ○ *mindfulness*
- ○ *mastery*

WEDNESDAY ____

- ○ *movement*
- ○ *mindfulness*
- ○ *mastery*

today's priorities

- •
- •
- •

today's priorities

- •
- •
- •

today's priorities

- •
- •
- •

What time are you going to bed tonight?

good night

THURSDAY ___

○ *movement*
○ *mindfulness*
○ *mastery*

FRIDAY ___

○ *movement*
○ *mindfulness*
○ *mastery*

SATURDAY ___

○ *movement*
○ *mindfulness*
○ *mastery*

today's priorities

●

●

●

today's priorities

●

●

●

today's priorities

●

●

●

SUNDAY ___

○ *movement*
○ *mindfulness*
○ *mastery*

today's priorities

●

●

●

reflection

reflection

SUNDAY	MONDAY	TUESDAY	WEDNESDAY

THURSDAY   FRIDAY   SATURDAY

MONTHLY GOALS FOR

*Make your annual goals more achievable with smaller steps
every month. Set those intentions here.*

GOOD MORNING MOMENTS

*When you capture these 3 moments every morning
you will consistently move toward the life you want!*

Movement

Mindfulness

Mastery

Events & Birthdays

/ /

/ /

/ /

/ /

/ /

/ /

/ /

People to reach out to

Reading

Watching

Planning

Learning

Ideas

MONDAY

○ movement
○ mindfulness
○ mastery

TUESDAY

○ movement
○ mindfulness
○ mastery

WEDNESDAY

○ movement
○ mindfulness
○ mastery

today's priorities

•

•

•

today's priorities

•

•

•

today's priorities

•

•

•

**What time are
you going to bed
tonight?**

good
night

THURSDAY ____

○ *movement*
○ *mindfulness*
○ *mastery*

FRIDAY ____

○ *movement*
○ *mindfulness*
○ *mastery*

SATURDAY ____

○ *movement*
○ *mindfulness*
○ *mastery*

today's priorities

•

•

•

today's priorities

•

•

•

today's priorities

•

•

•

SUNDAY ____

○ *movement*
○ *mindfulness*
○ *mastery*

today's priorities

•

•

•

MONDAY

○ movement
○ mindfulness
○ mastery

TUESDAY

○ movement
○ mindfulness
○ mastery

WEDNESDAY

○ movement
○ mindfulness
○ mastery

today's priorities

•

•

•

today's priorities

•

•

•

today's priorities

•

•

•

**What time are
you going to bed
tonight?**

good night

THURSDAY _____

○ *movement*
○ *mindfulness*
○ *mastery*

FRIDAY _____

○ *movement*
○ *mindfulness*
○ *mastery*

today's priorities

●

●

●

SATURDAY _____

○ *movement*
○ *mindfulness*
○ *mastery*

today's priorities

●

●

●

today's priorities

●

●

●

SUNDAY _____

○ *movement*
○ *mindfulness*
○ *mastery*

today's priorities

●

●

●

MONDAY ___

- ○ *movement*
- ○ *mindfulness*
- ○ *mastery*

TUESDAY ___

- ○ *movement*
- ○ *mindfulness*
- ○ *mastery*

WEDNESDAY ___

- ○ *movement*
- ○ *mindfulness*
- ○ *mastery*

today's priorities

- •
- •
- •

today's priorities

- •
- •
- •

today's priorities

- •
- •
- •

What time are you going to bed

tonight?

good night

THURSDAY _____

○ *movement*
○ *mindfulness*
○ *mastery*

FRIDAY _____

○ *movement*
○ *mindfulness*
○ *mastery*

SATURDAY _____

○ *movement*
○ *mindfulness*
○ *mastery*

today's priorities

•

•

•

today's priorities

•

•

•

today's priorities

•

•

•

SUNDAY _____

○ *movement*
○ *mindfulness*
○ *mastery*

today's priorities

•

•

•

MONDAY

○ movement
○ mindfulness
○ mastery

TUESDAY

○ movement
○ mindfulness
○ mastery

WEDNESDAY

○ movement
○ mindfulness
○ mastery

today's priorities

•

•

•

today's priorities

•

•

•

today's priorities

•

•

•

**What time are
you going to bed
tonight?**

good night

THURSDAY ____

○ *movement*
○ *mindfulness*
○ *mastery*

FRIDAY ____

○ *movement*
○ *mindfulness*
○ *mastery*

SATURDAY ____

○ *movement*
○ *mindfulness*
○ *mastery*

today's priorities

•

•

•

today's priorities

•

•

•

today's priorities

•

•

•

SUNDAY ____

○ *movement*
○ *mindfulness*
○ *mastery*

today's priorities

•

•

•

reflection

SUNDAY	MONDAY	TUESDAY	WEDNESDAY

THURSDAY   **FRIDAY**   **SATURDAY**

175

MONTHLY GOALS FOR _____

*Make your annual goals more achievable with smaller steps
every month. Set those intentions here.*

GOOD MORNING MOMENTS

*When you capture these 3 moments every morning
you will consistently move toward the life you want!*

Movement _____

_____

Mindfulness

Mastery _____

Events & Birthdays

/ /

/ /

/ /

/ /

/ /

/ /

/ /

People to reach out to

Reading

Watching

Planning

Learning

Ideas

MONDAY ___

○ movement
○ mindfulness
○ mastery

TUESDAY ___

○ movement
○ mindfulness
○ mastery

WEDNESDAY ___

○ movement
○ mindfulness
○ mastery

today's priorities

•

•

•

today's priorities

•

•

•

today's priorities

•

•

•

**What time are
you going to bed
tonight?**

good night

THURSDAY ___

○ *movement*
○ *mindfulness*
○ *mastery*

FRIDAY ___

○ *movement*
○ *mindfulness*
○ *mastery*

SATURDAY ___

○ *movement*
○ *mindfulness*
○ *mastery*

today's priorities

•

•

•

today's priorities

•

•

•

today's priorities

•

•

•

SUNDAY ___

○ *movement*
○ *mindfulness*
○ *mastery*

today's priorities

•

•

•

MONDAY	**TUESDAY**	**WEDNESDAY**
○ *movement*	○ *movement*	○ *movement*
○ *mindfulness*	○ *mindfulness*	○ *mindfulness*
○ *mastery*	○ *mastery*	○ *mastery*

today's priorities	*today's priorities*	*today's priorities*
•	•	•
•	•	•
•	•	•

What time are you going to bed

tonight?

good night

THURSDAY ___

○ *movement*
○ *mindfulness*
○ *mastery*

FRIDAY ___

○ *movement*
○ *mindfulness*
○ *mastery*

SATURDAY ___

○ *movement*
○ *mindfulness*
○ *mastery*

today's priorities

•

•

•

today's priorities

•

•

•

today's priorities

•

•

•

SUNDAY ___

○ *movement*
○ *mindfulness*
○ *mastery*

today's priorities

•

•

•

MONDAY ___

○ *movement*
○ *mindfulness*
○ *mastery*

TUESDAY ___

○ *movement*
○ *mindfulness*
○ *mastery*

WEDNESDAY ___

○ *movement*
○ *mindfulness*
○ *mastery*

today's priorities

•

•

•

today's priorities

•

•

•

today's priorities

•

•

•

*What time are
you going to bed*

tonight?

good
night

THURSDAY ___

- ○ *movement*
- ○ *mindfulness*
- ○ *mastery*

FRIDAY ___

- ○ *movement*
- ○ *mindfulness*
- ○ *mastery*

SATURDAY ___

- ○ *movement*
- ○ *mindfulness*
- ○ *mastery*

today's priorities

- •
- •
- •

today's priorities

- •
- •
- •

today's priorities

- •
- •
- •

SUNDAY ___

- ○ *movement*
- ○ *mindfulness*
- ○ *mastery*

today's priorities

- •
- •
- •

MONDAY ___

○ *movement*
○ *mindfulness*
○ *mastery*

TUESDAY ___

○ *movement*
○ *mindfulness*
○ *mastery*

WEDNESDAY ___

○ *movement*
○ *mindfulness*
○ *mastery*

today's priorities

-
-
-

today's priorities

-
-
-

today's priorities

-
-
-

What time are you going to bed tonight?

good night

THURSDAY ___

○ *movement*
○ *mindfulness*
○ *mastery*

FRIDAY ___

○ *movement*
○ *mindfulness*
○ *mastery*

SATURDAY ___

○ *movement*
○ *mindfulness*
○ *mastery*

today's priorities

•

•

•

today's priorities

•

•

•

today's priorities

•

•

•

SUNDAY ___

○ *movement*
○ *mindfulness*
○ *mastery*

today's priorities

•

•

•

reflection

reflection

LIKE THE PLANNER?
YOU'LL LOVE THE BOOK!

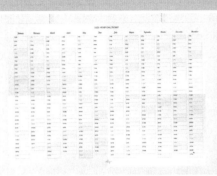

LTR
key

PLAN YOUR WAY

ltrkey.com
@ltr.key